Core Knowledge Language Arts

Scott
Unit 10 Reader

Skills Strand
KINDERGARTEN

Amplify learning.

Core Knowledge®

Copyright © 2013 Core Knowledge Foundation
www.coreknowledge.org

All Rights Reserved.

Core Knowledge Language Arts, Listening & Learning,
and Tell It Again! are trademarks of the Core Knowledge
Foundation.

Trademarks and trade names are shown in this book strictly
for illustrative and educational purposes and are the property
of their respective owners. References herein should not
be regarded as affecting the validity of said trademarks and
trade names.

Table of Contents
Scott
Unit 10 Reader

Scott and Lee

This is Scott Green. Scott is ten.

Scott's dad keeps a pig in a pen. Scott's mom keeps three hens. Scott keeps a sheep.

Lee the Sheep is Scott's pet. Scott feeds Lee and rubs him on the back. Lee is a sweet sheep.

Red Ants

Lee the Sheep had a bad week last week. Red ants bit him on his legs and feet.

Scott had to sweep the ants
with his hand to get rid of them.

Scott w*a*s mad at the ants.

"Ants," he said, "**Lee** is a sw**ee**t sh**ee**p. F**ee**l fr**ee** to munch on plants and w**ee**ds, but not on **Lee**!"

One of the ants said, "We f**ee**l bad. We will not munch on **Lee**. We will munch on plants and w**ee**ds."

The Bees

The red ants left. But then the b**ee**s got L**ee**! The b**ee**s stung L**ee** on his ch**ee**k and on his f**ee**t.

Scott ran up to help L**ee**. Then h<u>e</u> went and had a chat with the b**ee**s.

"Bees," said Scott, "why sting Lee the Sheep? He is a sweet sheep."

One bee said, "Bees will be bees."

One bee said, "I must be me."

Then Scott got mad. He said, "Sting the pig. Sting the hens! Sting the cat. Sting the dog. But let Lee be!" And the bees let Lee be.

Cake and Grapes

Scott got a cake to share with his pal Jade. Jade got a bunch of red grapes to share with Scott.

Scott went to Jade's and gave Jade the cake. Jade gave Scott the grapes. Then the kids sat and ate. Jade ate all of Scott's cake. Scott ate all of Jade's grapes.

Fun in the Sand

Scott is with Jade and Dave. The kids dig in the sand. They shape the sand. They make a sand man.

A big wave hits. The kids can't save their sand man from the wave. The sand man gets wet. He slumps. He sags. He drips.

The sand man is a mess. But the kids are not sad. They run and splash in the waves.

Skates

Jade got skates when she was six. Scott just got his last week. He is scared to get up on his skates.

"Is this safe?" Scott asks. "What if I trip and get a scrape? What if I hit a tree? What if I see a snake?"

"It is safe!" says Jade. "Just skate."

Jade helps Scott skate. Scott slips once. Then he gets the hang of it.

"Jade," he yells, "it's fun to skate!"

A Fine Hike

Scott is on a hike with Clive and Clive's dad. They hike three miles up a big hill.

At the top of the hill, Clive's dad says, "This is where we will camp." He drops his pack on the grass. Scott and Clive help him set up the tent.

At five, Scott and Clive hike to the lake to fish. They get five fish!

At dusk, the kids hike back to camp. Clive's dad makes a fire. The kids munch on hot dogs.

At nine, they get in their tent. They are all tired. They smile as they sleep.

The Bike Ride

Scott's sis, Meg, likes to ride a bike. Once Meg went on a bike ride with Scott. Meg's tire hit a rock and she fell off the bike.

Meg was brave. She did not yell. She did not sob. She got back on the bike. Then she said, "Let's ride!"

"Meg," Scott said, "I am glad my sis is so brave!"

That made Meg smile with pride!

The Plane Ride

Scott's dad rents a plane. He asks Scott and Meg to ride with him in the plane. The kids smile and nod.

The kids get in the plane. They click on their belts. Then their dad takes off. The plane picks up speed. By the time it gets to the end of the strip, it lifts up.

The kids can s**ee** lots of things fr<u>o</u>m the pl**ane**.

"That's Big L**a**k**e**!" says Scott. "But it's not s<u>o</u> big fr<u>o</u>m up h<u>ere</u>, is it? It s**ee**ms **like** it's just a frog pond!"

"<u>What</u>'s that?" Meg asks.

"That's a truck," says Scott.

"A truck?" says Meg. "But it's the s**ize** of a dot!"

Scott and Meg sm**ile**. It's fun to r**ide** in a pl**ane**.

The Gift

Scott and Meg's mom is named Liz. She stops off at Hope's Dress Shop.

"Hope," Liz says, "I need a doll's dress. The dress on Meg's doll has a bunch of holes in it."

"Well," says Hope, "here's a dress. It's a doll's size, and it's on sale."

"This is just <u>what</u> I n**ee**d!" says Liz. "It will fit Meg's doll, and Meg l**i**k**e**s gr**ee**n!"

H**o**p**e** drops the dress in a bag. Liz hands H**o**p**e** cash. H**o**p**e** hands the bag to Liz.

H**o**p**e** is glad. Sh<u>e</u> has m**a**d**e** a s**a**l**e**. Liz is glad, as well. Sh<u>e</u> has a gift to t**a**k**e** h**o**m**e** to Meg.

The Sled Ride

"I'll dri**ve**!" s<u>a</u>id Scott, as h<u>e</u> sat on the sled. J**a**d**e** and Meg got on next. D**a**v**e** w<u>a</u>s the last one on the sled. H<u>e</u> sat in back.

The sled slid off. It went fast.

"Scott," J**a**d**e** s<u>a</u>id, "st**ee**r to the left! Th<u>ere</u>'s a big st**one** th<u>ere</u> b<u>y</u> the—"

Smack! The sled hit the st**one**. The kids fell off.

Scott went to check on Jade.

"Ug!" Jade said. "I feel like I broke all the bones in my leg!"

"Hop on the sled," Scott said. "I will drag it home."

Meg went to check on Dave.

Dave said, "I froze my nose!"

"Hop on the sled with Jade," said Meg. "Scott and I will drag it home."

Scott's Snack Stand

Scott has a snack stand. Last week, he rode his bike to a shop to get nuts to sell at his stand. He got three big bags of nuts. The nuts cost him a lot of cash.

Scott slid the bags in his tote bag. Then he rode home.

When he got home, he got his mom to help him make hot spice nuts on the stove top.

Then Scott set up his stand.

"Hot sp*ice* nuts!" h<u>e</u> said. "Get a bag of hot sp*ice* nuts! Just one buck!"

A kid c**a**m**e** b<u>y</u> and got a bag of nuts. Then a man got a bag. Then the man's w**ife** got a bag. H<u>e</u> m**a**d**e** back the f**ive** h<u>e</u> had spent on nuts, plus ten in cash!

In the Pet Shop

Scott is in a pet shop. He spots a chimp in a pen. The chimp hangs from a branch. Then he jumps up on a big red **cube** and grins at Scott.

Scott sings a **tune** to the chimp. The chimp w**a**ve**s** back. Scott li**ke**s the chimp, and the chimp s**ee**ms to li**ke** him!

"Mom," Scott says, "this chimp is so cute. He got up on his cube and waved at me! Can I take him home?"

"No," says his mom. "My home is a chimp-free zone."

Scott stares at the chimp. His mom can see that he is sad, so she tells him he can get a fish.

Scott is so sad he can't take the chimp home, but he is glad he gets to take a fish home.

Scott Bakes a Cake

Scott's mom bakes cakes with Meg.

"Scott," she says, "you can help us with this cake, if you like."

Scott shrugs. "Well," he says, "if you can use my help, I will help."

"It will be fun," says his mom. "You can crack the eggs."

Scott cracks thr**ee** eggs and drops them in the dish.

Scott asks if he can mix up the eggs. Then he asks if he can add in the c**ake** mix.

"Well," his mom says, "if y<u>ou</u> add the c**ake** mix, then Meg gets to frost the c**ake**."

"Can I help Meg frost it?" Scott asks.

Mom and Meg sm**ile**.

Meg says, "S**ee**, Scott. It's fun to b**ake** a c**ake**!"

The Cave

Scott and Jade <u>are</u> on a hike. Jade spots a cave and peeks in.

"<u>Are</u> there bats in there?" Scott asks.

"I can't tell," Jade says, "but I hope so! I like bats!"

"Ick!" says Scott. "Bats are not cute."

Scott and Jade step in the cave.

Jade yells, "Bats, where are you? Wake up!"

Scott says, "Let the bats sleep."

Just then a bat glides up. It flaps its wings. It dips and spins.

Jade stares at the bat and smiles.

Scott ducks and yells, "Hide! A bat!"

The Skiff Ride

"Let's take a ride in my skiff," says Scott.

"What's a skiff?" asks Ling.

"Um, it's like a ship," says Scott, "but not so big."

The kids run to the dock. They can swim well, but, to be safe, they slip on life vests. Scott and Ling get in the skiff.

Scott st**ee**rs the skiff. He st**ee**rs it to the west s**ide** of the l**ake**. The skiff gl**ide**s in the wind.

Ling spots lots of fun things.

"I s**ee** ducks b**y** that p**ine** tr**ee**!" sh**e** yells.

"Is that a fish?" Scott asks.

"There's a cr**ane**!" Ling adds.

She says, "Scott, this is s**o** much fun!"

Lunch Trades

Dave checks his lunch bag. "No!" he fumes. "It's ham. I ate ham all week! Will you trade, Ling?"

"I'll trade my hot dog," Ling says, "but not my chips. Will you trade your lunch, Scott?"

"I will trade," Scott says, "but you will not like what Mom gave me."

"Why?" asks Ling. "What's in your bag?"

"A fish bone, a lump of fat, and a wet sock," says Scott.

"No to all of those!" says Ling.

"Ug!" says Dave. "No trade!"

As Ling and Dave trade, Scott keeps his bag. He does not tell Ling and Dave what he has in his bag. He has chips, ham, a bun, and a bunch of red grapes. Scott likes all of the things in his bag. He will not trade them.

Mike's Tale

The kids sat by a fire.

"Let's all tell tales," said Ling. "Then we can vote on which tale is the best!"

"Let me tell mine!" Mike said. "My tale will scare you."

"No!" said Dave, "You can't scare me!"

"Well," said Mike, "we will see!" "There's a Grump," Mike said, "that makes its home close to this spot. It's big. It has long fangs. It sleeps when the sun is up and wakes when the sun sets. The Grump can smell kids. It likes to grab them and .
. ."

Just then, there was a snap.

"What was that?" Dave said.

"It was just a twig," Ling said.

"But what made it snap like that?" said Dave.

Dave was scared.

"**EEEEEEEEEEEEEEEE**!" he said. "IT'S THE GRUMP! RUN! RUN FROM THE GRUMP!"

Dave got up to run, but Ling said, "It's not the Grump! It's just Meg!"

Green Grove Glade

Dave and Scott hike to Green Grove Glade with their moms and dads.

They stop at the gate and a man says, "Moms and dads, rest here where you can see your kids as they run, jump, and slide."

Scott and Dave are glad this is a spot for kids. They are glad their moms and dads are close if they get tired.

The kids swing on the swings. They slide on the slides. They ride on the rides. When they get tired, they get their moms and dads and hike back to their homes.

"Was it fun, Scott?" his mom asks when they get home.

Scott nods and smiles.

"What was it like?" she asks.

Scott grins and quips, "It was fun, Mom! Green Grove Glade is a fun spot for kids!"

The Boss

"Meg," Scott says, "when Mom and Dad are on their trip, I will be the boss here."

"You are not the boss of me!" says Meg.

"I'm the boss!" says Scott.

"You are not!" says Meg.

Scott glares at Meg. Meg glares back at him. Just then Mom steps in and taps Scott on the back. "Scott," she says, "meet Jen. Jen will be the boss till Dad and I get back."

"Meg's boss?" Scott asks.

"Meg's boss and Scott's boss," his mom says.

"Rats!" says Scott. "When will I get to be the boss?"

The King of Kites

"What's that?" Dave asks.

"It's a kite I made," says Scott.

"Can I help you test it?" Dave asks.

"Yes," says Scott.

The kids take the kite close to the lake to test it. Scott grabs the string. Then he runs as fast as he can.

The wind grabs Scott's kite. The kite zips up. It rides on the wind. It shines in the sun. The wind lifts it up till it is just a speck.

Dave cheers.

"Scott," he yells, "you are the man! That kite you made is the best kite of all time! You are the King of Kites!"

About This Book

This book has been created for use by students learning to read with the Core Knowledge Reading Program. Readability levels are suitable for early readers. The book has also been carefully leveled in terms of its "code load," or the number of spellings used in the stories.

The English writing system is complex. It uses more than 200 spellings to stand for forty-odd sounds. Many sounds can be spelled several different ways, and many spellings can be pronounced several different ways. This book has been designed to make early reading experiences simpler and more productive by using a subset of the available spellings. It uses *only* spellings students have been taught to sound out as part of their phonics lessons, plus a handful of tricky words, which have also been deliberately introduced in the lessons. This means the stories will be 100% decodable if they are assigned at the proper time.

As the students move through the program, they learn new spellings and the "code load" in the decodable readers increases gradually. The code load graphic on this page indicates the number of spellings students are expected to know in order to read the first story of the book and the number of spellings students are expected to know in order to read the final stories in the book. The columns on the inside back cover list the specific spellings and Tricky Words students are expected to recognize at the beginning of this reader. The bullets at the bottom of the inside back cover identify spellings, tricky words, and other topics that are introduced gradually in the unit this reader accompanies.

Visit us on the web at www.coreknowledge.org

CORE KNOWLEDGE LANGUAGE ARTS

SERIES EDITOR-IN-CHIEF
E. D. Hirsch, Jr.

PRESIDENT
Linda Bevilacqua

EDITORIAL STAFF
Carolyn Gosse, Senior Editor - Preschool
Khara Turnbull, Materials Development Manager
Michelle L. Warner, Senior Editor - Listening & Learning

Mick Anderson
Robin Blackshire
Maggie Buchanan
Paula Coyner
Sue Fulton
Sara Hunt
Erin Kist
Robin Luecke
Rosie McCormick
Cynthia Peng
Liz Pettit
Ellen Sadler
Deborah Samley
Diane Auger Smith
Sarah Zelinke

DESIGN AND GRAPHICS STAFF
Scott Ritchie, Creative Director

Kim Berrall
Michael Donegan
Liza Greene
Matt Leech
Bridget Moriarty
Lauren Pack

CONSULTING PROJECT MANAGEMENT SERVICES
ScribeConcepts.com

ADDITIONAL CONSULTING SERVICES
Ang Blanchette
Dorrit Green
Carolyn Pinkerton

ACKNOWLEDGMENTS
These materials are the result of the work, advice, and encouragement of numerous individuals over many years. Some of those singled out here already know the depth of our gratitude; others may be surprised to find themselves thanked publicly for help they gave quietly and generously for the sake of the enterprise alone. To helpers named and unnamed we are deeply grateful.

CONTRIBUTORS TO EARLIER VERSIONS OF THESE MATERIALS
Susan B. Albaugh, Kazuko Ashizawa, Nancy Braier, Kathryn M. Cummings, Michelle De Groot, Diana Espinal, Mary E. Forbes, Michael L. Ford, Ted Hirsch, Danielle Knecht, James K. Lee, Diane Henry Leipzig, Martha G. Mack, Liana Mahoney, Isabel McLean, Steve Morrison, Juliane K. Munson, Elizabeth B. Rasmussen, Laura Tortorelli, Rachael L. Shaw, Sivan B. Sherman, Miriam E. Vidaver, Catherine S. Whittington, Jeannette A. Williams

We would like to extend special recognition to Program Directors Matthew Davis and Souzanne Wright who were instrumental to the early development of this program.

SCHOOLS
We are truly grateful to the teachers, students, and administrators of the following schools for their willingness to field test these materials and for their invaluable advice: Capitol View Elementary, Challenge Foundation Academy (IN), Community Academy Public Charter School, Lake Lure Classical Academy, Lepanto Elementary School, New Holland Core Knowledge Academy, Paramount School of Excellence, Pioneer Challenge Foundation Academy, New York City PS 26R (The Carteret School), PS 30X (Wilton School), PS 50X (Clara Barton School), PS 96Q, PS 102X (Joseph O. Loretan), PS 104Q (The Bays Water), PS 214K (Michael Friedsam), PS 223Q (Lyndon B. Johnson School), PS 308K (Clara Cardwell), PS 333Q (Goldie Maple Academy), Sequoyah Elementary School, South Shore Charter Public School, Spartanburg Charter School, Steed Elementary School, Thomas Jefferson Classical Academy, Three Oaks Elementary, West Manor Elementary.

And a special thanks to the CKLA Pilot Coordinators Anita Henderson, Yasmin Lugo-Hernandez, and Susan Smith, whose suggestions and day-to-day support to teachers using these materials in their classrooms was critical.

CREDITS

Every effort has been taken to trace and acknowledge copyrights. The editors tender their apologies for any accidental infringement where copyright has proved untraceable. They would be pleased to insert the appropriate acknowledgment in any subsequent edition of this publication. Trademarks and trade names are shown in this publication for illustrative purposes only and are the property of their respective owners. The references to trademarks and trade names given herein do not affect their validity.

All photographs are used under license from Shutterstock, Inc. unless otherwise noted.

WRITERS
Matt Davis, Core Knowledge Staff

ILLUSTRATORS AND IMAGE SOURCES
All illustrations by Gail McIntosh